There is also strong evidence to show that many of the communications we regard as ICONIC or pictorial also require quite a lot of previous learning to understand. For example, in the 1950s a series of experiments was conducted with tribes in parts of Africa where there was dense bush or high grass. These people could not understand the devices of perspective that were common in European pictures. They simply did not use these as cues of depth or distance in their environment. Similarly, seemingly naturalistic drawings of elephants were not immediately recognized. The local technique for representing such creatures was to draw them as though they had been flattened on the ground with all four legs at right angles to the body.

There has been much discussion among theorists of an entirely pictorial language of communication. Semiotics is a term used to cover a whole field of study concerned with symbols. Charles Bliss devised the term sematography to describe his universal system of communication by symbols. This system is meant to be simple, logical and can be read in any language without translation.

Try for yourself to read the following messages in figures 1 and 2. The answers are at the end of this introduction. How universal are they?

Many labels involve a mixture of ICONIC or pictorial forms and SYMBOLIC or abstract forms. Most are not readily understood as a representational picture but rely on learning either of the whole symbol or symbol system and of the grammar that links pieces of a sign or symbol set together.

Another symbolic element which may be present in any label is colour. Certain colours are frequently used to convey particular messages. For example, red is commonly used for danger, green for safety, yellow for caution. More often colour is used to distinguish otherwise similar items, for example the coding of fire extinguishers to BS 5423. (See page 34). In this system the users must learn the code. It does not depend on any intuitive or iconic references. Colour in a label may increase its attractiveness or draw the attention of the audience but it will increase production costs and make the symbol hard to use in a variety of other applications.

3

Figure 1

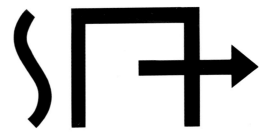

Figure 2

Examples:

Look at the following familiar signs on labels. Example 1 is quite pictorial. A male and a female figure denotes men's and women's toilets respectively. Look, however, at the amount of information that you have to assume:

- this means toilets;
- a man has his legs visible up to his trunk, a woman wears a skirt;
- men and women need to use separate toilets.

All of this information is necessary to get the message.

Example 2 is a roadsign. It shows the silhouette of a man walking and is surrounded by a red circle with a diagonal bar crossing the image. Although this sign is pictorial in one part you depend on the following for understanding:

- that the red circle denotes a road warning sign
- that the silhouette means a pedestrian
- that the diagonal red bar means a negative, i.e. NO PEDESTRIANS

Example 1

Example 2

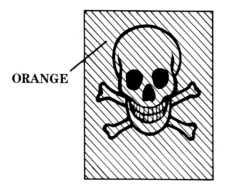

Example 3

Example 4

4

CONTENTS

1

INTRODUCTION

Consumers need information about the goods and services that they buy. They need – among other things – to know:

- what dangers and warnings are attached to a product
- how to maintain or to look after the product
- whether the product is safe and has been tested
- instructions for use including any assembly or fitting required
- what a product contains
- what are the consumers' rights and guarantees
- information about sizes, qualities, etc.
- about the quality of a product

The sheer volume of information required means that designers need to find ways to give it economically. With some small products the packaging instructions and labels could end up bigger than the goods themselves!

This book is about labels, their meaning, the reasons for their use and the symbols that they include. It is intended to help both consumers and designers to understand what labels mean and how they are developed. It is particularly useful for students of design/technology, home economics, and of business studies – especially those involved with mini-enterprise projects.

Designing a label

Designing a label for use on a consumer product is quite a complicated task. The label should be easy to read and to understand. It must be easy to produce within the technology available and it must be easy to attach to the product or its packaging. It must also meet the requirements of all of the laws and regulations necessary in the countries in which the product will be sold. In this book we deal only with British and European Community regulations. Each country has it own special labelling requirements – not least of which is that any written information and instructions should be in the language of the country concerned!

So, taking stock of the task of designing a label any of these discipline areas could – or should – be involved:

- perceptual psychology
- graphic design
- package design
- consumer research
- linguistics
- printing technology

Successful labels are those which communicate the intended message reasonably clearly to the intended audience.

Communication

We can communicate or represent ideas to people in three basic modes or forms:

ENACTIVE – this involves doing, showing or demonstrating. If you wish someone to know how to handle hazardous substances then you *show* them. You can teach the skills of using special tools, procedures, etc. by demonstration.

ICONIC – information can be set down in pictures. If these represent familiar objects then the user can see what to do almost as though you had given a demonstration. For example, how to repair a puncture shown in pictures.

SYMBOLIC – this is a more abstract kind of communication. You could use words, mathematical symbols, schematic diagrams, graphs etc.

Symbolic types of communication, rely more heavily on shared knowledge between the person trying to communicate a message and the receiver. To understand this written communication you must be able to:

- read using the Roman alphabet
- understand the English language
- understand specific words such as *label* or *symbol.*

All symbolic forms of communication depend on previous learning by the giver and receiver of the message. You must know the code and how to use it. There have been many studies into the kinds of learning needed. It is not simply a matter of learning the symbols themselves but also the grammar and the cultural background to the communication.

- that red is associated with danger and, hence warnings.

Example 3 denotes hazardous chemicals. The background colour is orange. The key to understanding the sign is the skull and crossbones motif. This has been used in Europe and America to denote death and/or danger – especially associated with poisons. But is this true the world over? Is it specific to certain cultures? Again there is a lot of scope for alternative interpretation.

Example 4 is a completely different approach. The label means that the package is fragile and must not be dropped or roughly handled. The wineglass is a visible metaphor for breakage. It is unlikely that the case is filled with wineglasses, so a literal interpretation of the image is impossible. The following steps to understanding are needed.

- Recognition of the wineglass
- Knowledge that wineglasses are fragile and easily broken
- By association, recognise that the package contents are fragile and easily broken.

In this way we can see that apparently pictorial signs, symbols and labels require some degree of background knowledge to interpret them. They have both iconic and symbolic elements.

For these reasons we can take nothing for granted in developing a label for particular use. We may look at symbol dictionaries and choose appropriate forms but we must always incorporate research into users' actual perceptions of what is meant by the label.

Standards – whether British, foreign, European or international are ways in which symbols are recorded and communicated. They are agreed by committees of experts and are used in place of other possible solutions. Over the years they are learned and used so that they become a common language of communication. One function of this book is to show some of the symbols that are set down in standards (and elsewhere) and to show what they mean.

Answers to Bliss Symbols:
Figure 1 Cinema   **Figure 2** Fire exit

The process of devising an information label consists of these steps.

1 Writing out clearly and simply the message that the label must convey so that it can be easily understood.
2 Describing the audience for the label and what they need to know.
3 Deciding whether a symbol should be used.
4 Deciding the format – swing-tag, sew-in label, moulding etc.
5 Looking at existing symbols or pictograms that could be used.
6 Developing symbols that you could use.
7 Trialling the symbols with users to see how easily they understand what is meant.
8 Repeating steps 5 and 6 if a symbol is chosen.
9 Putting symbols and written text together.
10 Production.

For example, the symbol for drinking water was designed as an internationally recognised label for taps or other water sources. This is now specified in British Standard BS 6034.

The symbol was chosen following a proper development and trial. When the message was devised a search was made for existing symbols. A panel of experts looked at the collection (see figure 4) and selected three: 7,8 and 11 for more intensive research. Consumers were shown each symbol and asked to say what they meant. These were the results (see figure 3).

The final choice of symbol was number 11 which achieved the highest percentage of correct responses and had no really outlandish suggestions as to its meaning. The elements of the chosen symbol are :

- a tap
- a tumbler shape
- wavy lines to indicate water in the tumbler.

Any label can be put through a similar user trial.

	%		%		%
CORRECT	41	CORRECT	38	CORRECT	67
TAP	22	REFRESHMENTS	8	WATER	12
DRINK	—	DRINKING FACILITIES	14	TAP	9
WATER MAINS	2	BAR/DRINKS	13	BAR/DRINKS	1
WASH ROOM	2	WATER	2	REFRESHMENTS	1
FIRE HYDRANT	2	DRINKS SOLD	1	TAP WITH GLASS	1
WATER	22				
OTHERS	8	OTHERS	14	OTHERS	7
DON'T KNOW	1	DON'T KNOW	5	DON'T KNOW	2

Figure 3

Project ideas

1 Design appropriate labelling for a simple piece of apparatus in the school, a sign to emphasize a school rule or a label for a product such as a toy designed in CDT or home economics, for example:

- do not touch,
- keep off the grass
- the different subjects on your school timetable to label books and other materials
- wash care labels for a garment made in Home Economics/fashion design.

For each, investigate recognition of the label including differences between groups (such as different ages, sexes or cultures) in the perception of signs and symbols.

Investigate the most effective colours for the label. For example, we know that black and yellow are nature's warning colours but will they still work in your design?

2 Design a set of 'wordless' instructions as a label for a particular product or piece of equipment. Pupils should only use diagrams. Investigate the way people use these. Incorporate the results of the investigation into the design and produce a universal set of instructions to be printed on an attached label or on the packaging of the product.

3 Ask pupils to collect labels from various food-stuffs. Remove the product name and type and then identify the food product from the list of ingredients.

Useful reference sources

- *Art and Visual Perception*, Rudolph Arnheim, Faber and Faber, London 1956.
- *Art and Illusion: A study of the Psychology of Pictorial Representation*, E H Gombrich, Phadon, 1960.
- *Learning and Visual Communication*, David Sless, Croom Helim, London, 1981.
- *Man and his symbols*, Carl G Jung et al., Dell Publishing Co, New York, 1968.
- *International Picture Language*, Otto Newrath, Kegan Paul, London, 1936.
- *Sematography*, Charles K Bliss, Sematography Publications, Sydney, Australia.

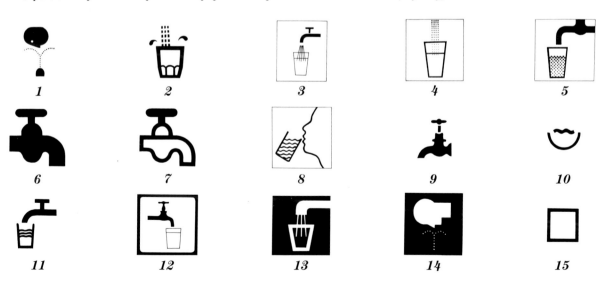

1 2 3 4 5

6 7 8 9 10

11 12 13 14 15

Figure 4

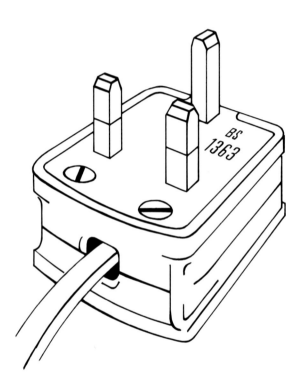

COMPLIANCE WITH BRITISH STANDARDS

COMPLIANCE WITH BRITISH STANDARDS

The British Standards Institution has more than 10,000 Standards covering a wide range of goods and services. Each Standard has an identifying number such as BS 1363 for 13 amp electric plugs and unswitched sockets. When you see a BS number or a statement such as 'Complies with BS ...' this is the manufacturer's claim to have complied with the standard in the production of an item. The standard may refer to the safety, performance or dimensions of a product, or any combination of these; e.g. BS 1363 specifies the requirements for 13 A plugs and switched and unswitched socket-outlets to ensure their safety, satisfactory performance and interchangeability. They should be made from materials that do not break easily or distort in normal use and there should be protection against touching live pins when the plug is being fitted into the socket.

In the event of traders making false claims of compliance they may be prosecuted under the Trade Descriptions Act. Trading Standards Officers, employed by local authorities, are able to advise consumers about individual complaints.

Standards are generally used voluntarily. However in some cases Government regulations require compliance with a British Standard. For example, the Toys (Safety) Regulations 1989, require toys to be made to BS 5665, the British Standard for the *Safety of toys*.

THE KITEMARK

Standards specify the requirements for a huge range of products. BSI offers independent assurance that a manufacturer's claim of compliance with a particular British Standard is true. This is done through BSI certification schemes, which enable products to be marked with BSI's own widely recognized trademark, the Kitemark, through a carefully controlled licensing process.

The Kitemark on a product means that BSI has carried out independent testing of samples of the product against the appropriate British Standard and confirmed that the standard has been met in every respect. The manufacturer must also be able to show that the quality procedures being used in his factory meet the requirements of another standard, BS 5750 for quality management systems.

When a manufacturer applies for a Kitemark licence BSI staff visit the factory to assess the quality assurance arrangements. This establishes that the manufacturer is capable of consistently producing to the standard. The product is then tested independently to check the manufacturer's claim of compliance with the relevant British Standard.

A licence to use the Kitemark is issued when all requirements are satisfied. Manufacturers are then allowed to show the Kitemark on a product, together with any other information relevant to the standard. Factories in the United Kingdom and abroad are licensed to apply the Kitemark to several thousand different types and models of products.

The first Kitemark licence was issued in 1926 to the General Electric Company for industrial reflector fittings for electric street lighting made to BS 232. The oldest Kitemark licence still in operation dates from the late 1930s. It is for road vehicle safety glass.

Although any manufacturer can claim compliance with a British Standard and use words to this effect on a product, only Kitemark licensees are able to provide BSI's assurance that such claims are valid.

Following the issue of a licence the manufacturer can expect unannounced visits from BSI inspectors, who will check that compliance with the standard is being maintained. During these visits the inspector will select random samples from the production line to take away for independent testing.

Buying Kitemarked goods gives the purchaser assurance that goods meet the standard. It also creates confidence because BSI is committed to following up any problems relating to goods which bear the Kitemark.

Some consumer products which may bear the Kitemark are :

gas and oil burning appliances
aluminium windows
Christmas tree lights
contraceptive condoms and diaphragms
ladders
life-jackets
protective helmets
gas cookers
WC seats

12

THE SAFETY MARK

THE SAFETY MARK

This mark appears on a number of products which meet the safety requirements of particular British Standards.

As with the Kitemark, the Safety Mark can only be used by manufacturers licensed under a Safety Scheme which involves a scheme of strict quality control procedures. This mark may appear on some luminaires, typewriters and other office machinery.

The Safety Mark came about as a result of EEC requirements for the safety of electrical equipment. It was necessary to develop a new and different mark for safety only, since the Kitemark can certify, for example, that a pipe is the right strength and size, in addition to safety factors.

Although resembling the lower half of a matchstick man the white lines on the triangular group draw the outline of the initials BSI.

SYMBOL FOR BSI REGISTERED FIRMS

SYMBOL FOR BSI REGISTERED FIRMS

The British Standards Institution runs a system for the Registration of Firms of Assessed Capability. This gives independent assurance of a firm's ability to produce to standard specifications, whether they be national, international, company or customer standards.

To carry out the assessment a team of experts will visit a firm and investigate its ability to meet the requirements of BS 5750 *Quality systems* and a Quality Assessment Schedule designed to apply BS 5750 to the particular processes involved. If successful, the firm is registered and then visited several times a year to ensure that the quality assurance system is still operating satisfactorily.

BSI's Register of Assessed Firms is principally used by purchasing organizations who wish to assure themselves of a firm's capability before placing orders for goods or services. Many companies throughout the world will only deal with other quality assured sources so that their quality is maintained. Major purchasers in central and local government also want quality assured companies to undertake contracts. This is a fast-growing area of BSI's work at home and abroad.

SYMBOL FOR BSI REGISTERED STOCKISTS

SYMBOL FOR BSI REGISTERED STOCKISTS

BSI also runs a system for registering Stockists of Assessed Capability. Stockists who buy from quality assured sources, who have thorough administration and efficient stock identification can apply for registration under this scheme.

As with the Registered Firms Scheme BSI assesses the company's documented quality system to ensure that it meets the requirements of BS 5750 *Quality Systems*, conducts a site assessment and, after registration, carries out surveillance visits.

16

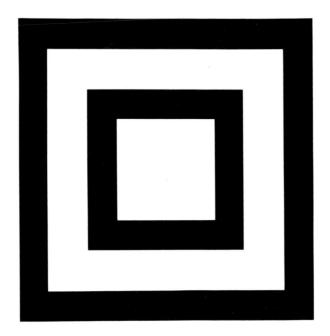

DOUBLE INSULATION OF ELECTRICAL APPLIANCES

DOUBLE INSULATION OF ELECTRICAL APPLIANCES

This mark is found on a particular class of electrical goods which are built in a special way without any provision for earthing but with double insulation and/or reinforced insulation throughout.

The user should take care to connect the flexible cord correctly to the plug. There are only two wires to worry about:

BROWN WIRE – LIVE TERMINAL
BLUE WIRE – NEUTRAL TERMINAL

Absolutely no connection must be made to the earth terminal of the plug.

This mark is frequently seen on products like hair-dryers, portable tools and vacuum cleaners. It may be seen beside the BEAB mark.

**BEAB
Approved**

BEAB MARK

Equipment bearing this mark has been approved as safe by the British Electrotechnical Approvals Board (BEAB).

The mark means that samples of the product have been tested to the requirements of the appropriate National Harmonized Standard and that the sample complies with the Low Voltage Electrical Equipment (Safety) Regulations 1989.

Before BEAB approval for any product is granted the factory must satisfy BEAB's requirement for Safety Testing, Quality Control and Inspection. Surveillance testing of samples and inspections of the place of manufacture continue throughout the life of an approval.

The mark must be permanently displayed on or near the rating plate and may also be found on swing labels attached to the equipment.

20

CE MARK

Free trade in the Single European Market depends on common legal, technical and safety standards being met. The European Commission has prepared directives for a wide range of products and services which set out the essential safety requirements. Manufacturers must meet the essential safety requirements set down in these directives and must show this by marking their products with the letters CE.

Unlike schemes such as the Kitemark, the CE mark does not have a programme of testing or surveillance. Any manufacturer who believes that his products comply may use the mark. However, where goods are found not to meet the requirements they can be seized and the manufacturer, importer or supplier could be prosecuted.

The main use of the mark is by customs and excise staff and by agencies such as trading standards departments who monitor trade and ensure that legal requirements are met.

Only about 15% of products are or will be covered by directives. Each separate area has its own timetable for introducing the mark. The first scheme, for toys, was introduced in 1990.

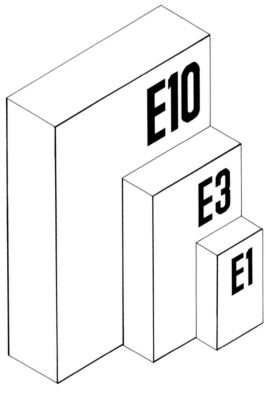

3.1kg   **930g** **310g**
7700ml   2250ml   750ml

EUROSIZE PACKETS FOR FABRIC WASHING POWDERS (E SIZES)

EUROSIZE PACKETS FOR FABRIC WASHING POWDERS (E SIZES)

In 1975 the packaging for fabric washing powders changed to the system known as E sizes (Eurosize packs). These packages are based on a sequence of packet volumes. The smallest size, E1, has a packet with an internal volume of 750 mL. Subsequent sizes are multiples of this, e.g.
E3 − 2250 mL and
E10 − 7700 mL (7500 plus 200 mL for the inclusion of a measuring cup).

These sizes were formally established by the European Committee for Standardization, or CEN (Comité Européen de Normalisation). CEN members are drawn from standards organizations throughout Europe. The countries involved are Austria, Belgium, Denmark, Finland, France, Germany, Ireland, Italy, Netherlands, Norway, Portugal, Spain, Sweden, Switzerland and the United Kingdom. CEN produced the Standard EN 23: *Packages for washing and cleaning powders* Part 1 1978 − *Dimensions and volumes of cartons and drums from fibreboard*. In the United Kingdom this standard appeared as BS 5167 *Packages for washing and cleaning powders. Dimensions and volumes of cartons and drums from fibreboard*.

Packets of washing powder often feature the word 'Eurosize' and 'E size' to avoid confusion with the small 'e' mark.

The weight of different powders varies because the various brands of washing powder may have different densities. Some powders are heavier than others and therefore are packed at somewhat greater weight for the same volume.

To allow comparison of price/weight, when the UK detergent industry moved to the E size volumes, they also packed in multiples of weight. In other words, for any one brand an E10 pack would contain ten times an E1 or three and a third times the E3 pack. For example, for an E3 packet of automatic washing powder containing 930 g, the equivalent E10 would contain 3.1 kg.

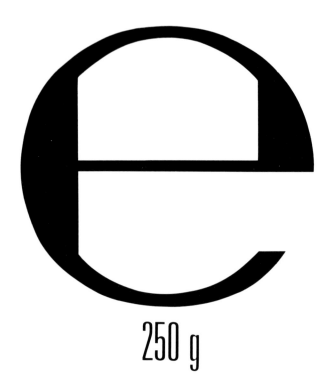

250 g

THE 'e' MARK

Until 1 January 1980 most packages sold by retail had to contain at least the quantity stated.

After that date a new system was introduced known as The Average System of Weights and Measures. The 'e' mark indicates that this system is being used. It was introduced as a result of Common Market membership to bring UK practice into line with those of other Member States, and indeed most countries throughout the world. The 'e' mark acts as a metrological passport throughout the whole of the EEC.

Packages made up to a fixed, predetermined weight or volume of the contents must be marked with that weight or volume (the 'nominal quantity') and three rules must be observed:

- The contents of the packages must not be less on average than the nominal quantity.

- Not more than one package in 40 may contain less than the nominal quantity by more than an amount known as the tolerable negative error. This varies according to the quantity and is laid out in official tables.

- No packages are allowed to contain less than the nominal quantity by more than twice the tolerable negative error.

Note: In the example given on the card for a package containing 250 g, the tolerable negative error is 9 g.

The mark must be at least 3 mm high and be placed in the same field of vision as the nominal quantity.

Previously, the seller or retailer was responsible for ensuring correct measure. Now, the packer or importer is responsible for the quantity and will usually have to be able to produce records of production checks to show an inspector. A shopkeeper will now commit an offence only if he knowingly sells packages infringing rule 3 above.

Complaints should be reported to the local Trading Standards Department.

5 012345 678900

BARCODES

A barcode is a symbol printed on packages which identifies goods in a form which can be read electronically and transmitted to a computer.

In the UK the article number which appears beneath the barcode is administered by the Article Number Association (UK) Limited. Members of ANA are allocated a manufacturer's reference number and then a block of digits so that every unit of sale – every variation in size, colour and pack – has a unique and separate identifying mark, as follows:

50	12345	6789	0
Country code	Manufacturer's reference	Product number	Check digit

Computerized point-of-sale equipment is now installed in a number of stores and barcodes are read electronically at the checkout. The scanner transmits the product number to an in-store computer. This relays the product's description and current price back to the checkout, where the information is displayed electronically, and simultaneously printed on the till receipt for the customer. The in-store computer then deducts that item from the stock list so that re-ordering can be automated.

The benefits for customers include :

- quicker checkout service
- itemized till receipts, identifying each purchase and its price
- virtual elimination of checkout errors
- in the long term, fewer out-of-stocks and lower prices than otherwise possible, from more efficient store operation
- a system catering for price discounts more easily, where offered, on bulk purchases.

The benefits for industry include, in addition:

- better communication between manufacturer and retailer
- faster re-ordering enabling reductions in storage space
- improved stock control

Barcoded packs will not necessarily be individually price marked but there is a legal obligation to display prices conspicuously and unambiguously. The ANA recommends that prices of all items sold in a store should be displayed clearly, probably in the form of a distinctive shelf-edge label.

Where a product number is discontinued, three years must elapse before the same number can be reallocated to a different product.

Food manufacturers were the first to use barcodes but they now appear on many other products, including detergents, books, records, clothing and pharmaceuticals.

Further information is available from the Article Number Association, 6 Catherine Street, London WC2B 5JJ. Tel: 071 – 836 2460

28

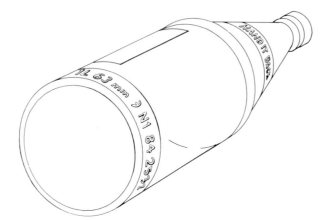

A bottle may have on its label an 'e' marked with the capacity, in litres if over one litre, and in centilitres or millilitres if under one litre. In some cases capacity may be shown in imperial units as well.

New bottles made in accordance with the British Standards issued must also have a number of markings moulded into the bottle, including – rather confusingly – a different kind of 'e'!

The 'e' mark confirms that the bottle is also a measuring container, and meets the requirements of the Measuring Container Regulations (1977). Glass manufacturers must check and record the capacity of the bottle. A permanent statement of its mean, or nominal capacity, must be marked – usually by engraving the mould. Also the distance from the top of the bottle to the liquid level, to which this capacity relates, is shown. This is the filling level. This means that the packer, who is responsible for guaranteeing that the bottle has been filled with the correct amount of liquid, can simply check the liquid level with a template. (Wine bottles may be marked on the bottom instead of on the side of the insweep.)

Beer, cider and soft drinks bottles should have a returnability marking on the shoulder. In the case of beer and cider the recommended message is 'Please return' but for the other types 'Hand it back'.

Many milk bottles have some of these markings, including the 'e' mark, nominal capacity and filling level.

HARMFUL SUBSTANCES

Certain substances in everyday use in the home can be dangerous if not used properly, for example certain bleaches (sodium hypochlorite), caustic soda, kettle descaler (formic acid), paraffin, etc.

To protect the user, the Packaging and Labelling of Dangerous Substances Regulations 1984 require these substances to be clearly labelled with a warning symbol, a keyword and phrases indicating the risks involved and the safety precautions to follow. Listed substances are classified as dangerous under either one or two of the following hazard categories:

(a) explosive, oxidizing, extremely flammable, highly flammable or flammable (i.e. fire or explosion hazards); or

(b) very toxic, toxic, corrosive, harmful or irritant (health hazards).

Two examples of the labelling required under the regulations from category (b) are:

Irritant refers to non-corrosive substances which through contact can, for example, cause reddening or blistering of the skin. This sign is also used for harmful substances. It may be found on some bottles of bleach.

Corrosive refers to substances which on contact with living tissues may destroy them. The indication of particular risks and of safety precautions required may vary according to the substance.

In addition to labelling requirements, the Regulations impose a general requirement for the container of the substance to be designed, constructed and secured so as to prevent any of the contents escaping when subjected to the stresses and strains of normal handling.

The Regulations include pure substances and mixtures, prepared by the manufacturer, of two or more substances. There is also provision for pesticides, solvents and paints, varnishes, printing inks, adhesives and similar products.

(Illustrated on page 32)

30

Health and safety at work

Health and Safety standards for school premises are set out in the Education (School Premises) Regulations 1981. These include requirements of site, structural stability, fire precautions, lighting, heating, ventilation, etc.

Many substances used in school laboratories and workshops are harmful. For example:

- substances labelled corrosive, irritant, harmful, toxic or very toxic
- products or by-products (dust, fumes, etc)
- micro-organisms (viruses, bacteria, etc)
- carcinogens (cancer-causing agents)

The Control of Substances Hazardous to Health (COSHH) Regulations 1988 protect users from hazardous substances at work. The Regulations impose duties on employers to protect employees. Employers are required to conduct an assessment to determine:

- which substances are present
  which substances are people exposed to every day and which only now and then?
- How each substance is used
  How is each substance handled, stored etc?
- The risks of health
  Could death, illness or injury result from one exposure, short-term exposure or long-term exposure?
- The hazards of each substance
  Could a substance be swallowed, inhaled or absorbed through the skin?
- Who is exposed to hazardous substances?
  Are pupils, technicians, visitors and others at risk?

The Regulations also require employers to take steps to prevent or, where this is not possible to control the exposure of hazardous substances. For example to prevent exposure a substance may be removed from use or be substituted by a less hazardous substance. Exposure could be controlled by the use of ventilation or by reducing the length or level of exposure.

Further information about COSHH or health and safety at work can be obtained from:

- local offices of the Health and Safety Executive or Environmental Health Department
  (look in the phone book for the nearest office)
- Department of Education and Science publications:

Safety in Science Laboratories
Safety in Practical Studies
Safety in Further Education
These are available from HMSO, 49 High Holborn, London WC1V 6HB.

CAUSTIC SODA

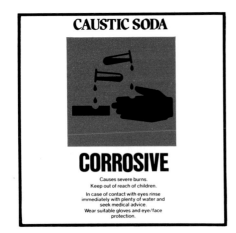

CORROSIVE

Causes severe burns.
Keep out of reach of children.

In case of contact with eyes rinse
immediately with plenty of water and
seek medical advice.
Wear suitable gloves and eye/face
protection.

SODIUM HYPOCHLORITE

IRRITANT

Contact with acids liberates toxic gas
irritating to eyes and skin.

Keep out of reach of children.

Avoid contact with eyes.

Model BS4

nu-swift

HARLAND

Lic. No. 6556

2.5kg Halon (Stored Pressure) Fire Extinguisher

 **Use upright
Pull out clip**

 **Hold nozzle
Squeeze lever**

Aim at fire

For temporary shut-off: release lever
Recharge after complete or partial use

Fire Test Rating: 5A:55B

For use on:
CLASS A FIRES – Wood, paper, textiles etc.
CLASS B FIRES – Flammable liquids.
CLASS C FIRES – Flammable gases.

Suitable for electrical risks
Suitable for use between $-30°C$ and $+60°C$

CONTENTS: 2.5kg Bromochlorodifluoromethane pressurised with
nitrogen. Working pressure (at 20°C) 10 bar. Test pressure 30 bar.

INSPECTION: Once a month inspect for obvious damage.
Inspect pressure gauge. If needle is in 'recharge' sector, return
complete extinguisher to suppliers for recharging.

MAINTENANCE: This extinguisher should be serviced annually by a
Nu-Swift service engineer or other competent person.

RECHARGING: After complete or partial use return complete
extinguisher to suppliers for recharging.

WARNING: The fumes given off are dangerous especially in a confined
space.

This extinguisher should be recharged in accordance with BS 6643:
Part 1 by a competent person.

NU-SWIFT INTERNATIONAL LTD., ELLAND, WEST YORKS., ENGLAND
Telephone Elland (0422) 72852 & 76811 Telex 51.384

1704790.BO

COVER FABRIC
NOT MATCH RESISTANT

CAUTION

RESISTANT

All
filling
materials
meet the 1988
safety regulations

CAUTION

FIRE EXTINGUISHERS

FIRE EXTINGUISHERS

BS 5423 *Specification for portable fire extinguishers* requires portable fire extinguishers to be marked with the content e.g. 'water', 'foam', 'powder', 'carbon dioxide' or 'halon'; the type e.g. 'gas cartridge' or 'stored pressure'. The class of fire for which the extinguisher is suitable is also marked :

Class A — wood, paper, textiles, etc
Class B — liquids
Class C — gases

Instructions for use and warnings as appropriate e.g. 'Do not use on electrical equipment' should be clearly marked.

Extinguishers can be colour coded so that their type can be easily recognized. BS 5423 recommends three methods:

a) coloured predominantly signal red with a colour-coded label indicating the type, or

b) colour-coded entirely by content type using the system below, or

c) of self-coloured metal with a colour-coded label indicating the type and advises that any other system used should not conflict with these.

Colour Coding by Content Type	
Content Type	**Colour**
Water	**Signal Red**
Foam	**Pale Cream**
Powder (all types)	**French Blue**
Carbon Dioxide	**Black**
Halon	**Emerald Green**

(Illustrated on page 32)

BAFE symbol

British Approvals for Fire Equipment (BAFE) is a Government recognized national organization for the promotion of quality assurance for fire protection equipment.

The BAFE symbol means that fire extinguishers have been made to British Standard specifications and tested and assessed by independent experts from BSI and the Loss Prevention Certification Board.

34

FLAMMABILITY OF FURNITURE

Upholstered furniture for the domestic market must be labelled to show consumers that it has been tested for flammability. The tests used are found in the first part of BS 5852 *Fire tests for furniture*. The first of these tests is the effect of a smouldering cigarette. Furniture failing this test has now been banned. The second test is for the ignitability of furniture when subjected to a flame equivalent to a lighted match. From 1 March 1990 all furniture offered for sale in the domestic market must also pass the match test.

The Government Regulations are the Furniture and Furnishings (Fire)(Safety) Regulations 1988 S.I. No. 1324 and the Furniture and Furnishings (Fire) (Safety)(Amendment) Regulations 1989 S.I. No. 2358. If a local Trading Standards Officer considers that there has been an infringement of the regulations and that a piece of furniture is dangerous he may issue a prohibition order banning further sales.

Note that these Regulations only apply to new up-holstered seating including garden furniture but not bedding, stools or other types of furniture and to second hand furniture in certain circumstances. (Part 2 of BS 5852, which is not invoked in these Regulations, specifies tests for the effect from heat sources greater than a match up to the equivalent of four double sheets of newspaper.)

(Illustrated on page 33)

INTERNATIONAL SYMBOL OF DEAFNESS

INTERNATIONAL SYMBOL OF DEAFNESS

The International Symbol of Deafness is used by those people with impaired hearing to indicate the need for sympathetic understanding of their communication needs.

The symbol is also used to indicate access and facilities for the deaf and hard of hearing and is seen in shops, offices, hospitals, theatres and in many other places which have taken the trouble to provide support facilities.

The symbol is widely publicized, and can be recognized by the distinctive burgundy colour of the Sympathetic Hearing Scheme which is administered by the British Association of the Hard of Hearing. The Scheme provides support and encouragement to the hearing impaired.

37

38

TACTILE DANGER WARNINGS

TACTILE DANGER WARNINGS

Blind and visually handicapped people need help in finding out whether the contents of a package are harmless or dangerous. BS 7280 *Requirements for tactile danger warnings for packaging* improves the physical protection of consumers by specifying a tactile danger warning on packagings which are intended for certain dangerous substances. These do not include pharmaceutical products.

The tactile symbol can be found on the product packaging and not on any secondary packaging e.g. cardboard box protecting a glass bottle.

39

ACCESS SYMBOLS

The International Access Symbol is used in buildings where provision for disabled people is made. The sign can be displayed to show the whereabouts of convenient facilities and to identify and advertise the following:

- accessible entrances to buildings
- manageable routes through buildings
- accessible lifts
- accessible lavatory accommodation
- reserved car-parking spaces
- the availability of special services in buildings.

BS 5810 *Code of Practice for Access for the disabled to buildings* details basic architectural features necessary to make buildings convenient for use by disabled people.

CRISPS

ready
salted

5 012345 678900

C R FOODS
PO BOX No. 8
SOLIHULL
W MIDLANDS

BEST BEFORE

09 FEB 1992

28 g e

Ingredients: Potatoes,
Vegetable Oil and
Hydrogenated Vegetable
Oil, Salt

In 1980 UK regulations for the labelling of food were introduced implementing the EEC food labelling Directive 79/112 EEC. The regulations lay down detailed requirements for the labelling of foodstuffs in order to prohibit misleading labelling, advertizing and presentation of food so as to give greater protection to the consumer. These regulations were subsequently superseded by the Food Labelling Regulations 1984 which came fully into effect from 1 July 1986.

Labelling includes any words, particulars, trade mark, brand name, pictorial matter or symbol relating to the food.

Foods which are ready for delivery to the consumer or to a catering establishment must be marked with:

(i)   the name of the food − not merely a brand name, trade mark or fancy name

(ii) a list of ingredients, including permitted additives, must be shown in descending order of inclusion, by weight. If added water accounts for more than 5% of the contents, it also counts as an ingredient. Claims for an especially large or small quantity of a particular ingredient must be demonstrated by including its weight. An additive may be shown by name or E-number. The E-number is an officially accepted code which applies throughout Europe.

(iii) an indication of minimum durability expressed in terms of day, month, year. This means the date up to and including which food can reasonably be expected to remain at its best, if properly stored. On most prepacked foods a 'best before' date is stated. Perishable foods, intended for consumption within six weeks, may also be seen with a label marked 'use-by' (date) and an indication of maximum durability after purchase.

(iv) any special storage conditions or conditions of use

(v)   the name or business name and address or registered office of the manufacturer, packer or seller within the EEC

(vi) place of origin of food, if lack of such information could materially mislead the consumer.

(vii) instructions for preparation if necessary.

Some foods do not have to list ingredients, e.g. whole, unpeeled fresh fruit and vegetables, any food consisting of a single product or drinks with an alcoholic strength by volume of more than 1.2%.

Other foods are exempted from the need to bear a date mark e.g. fresh fruit and vegetables which have not been peeled or cut into pieces; drinks with an alcoholic strength of 10% or more by volume; bread or flour confectionery normally sold within 24 hours of preparation; deep frozen food and food with a minimum durability of more than 18 months.

Foods which claim to have special properties, e.g. slimming aids, vitamin rich foods, nutritional value for infants or diabetics, must be labelled with additional particulars to support the claim.

The quantity or weight of the product must be shown on labels. This will often be accompanied by the 'e' mark explained earlier.

A booklet 'Look at the Label' can be obtained from: Food Sense, London, SE99 7TT.
A 12-minute audio-visual programme, 'Look at the Label', on 16 mm film or videocassette is available on free loan or for sale from any of the following libraries:

CSL Vision
PO Box 35
Wetherby
West Yorkshire
LS23 7EX
Tel: 0937 541010

Welsh Office Film Library
Crown Building
Cathays Park
Cardiff
CF1 3NQ
Tel: 0222 8251111

Scottish Central Film Library
74 Victoria Crescent Road
Glasgow
G12
Tel: 041-334 9314

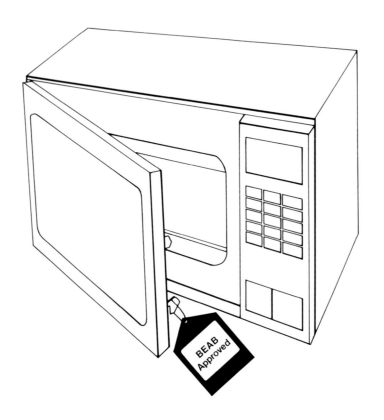

BEAB
Approved

BS 3456 *Safety of household and similar electrical appliances* Part 102 *Particular requirements* Section 102.25 *Appliances for heating food by means of microwave energy*, sets out the requirements for the safety of this equipment. The maximum level of radiation leakage tolerated is an energy flux density of 50 W/m² at any point 5 cm or more from the external surface of the appliance.

Tests are carried out under different conditions, amongst which are the following:

(i) The door is opened and closed 100 000 times. This is the equivalent of using the oven 7 times a week, 52 weeks a year for almost 40 years. Measurements of radiation leakage are taken after each 10 000 operations.

(ii) There is a minimum of two fail safe switches which must cut out automatically if the oven door is opened from its closed position.

(iii) Mechanical strength tests are carried out on the doors so that even if the oven is knocked it should continue to operate normally.

(iv) Even when the door seals are contaminated with oil, or a piece of paper 0.1 mm to 0.2 mm thick is placed between the oven door and cooking cavity, the radiation leakage must not exceed the level previously specified.

Other tests include those for heat and fire resistance, electrical insulation and stability.

When a domestic microwave oven has passed these tests, it may be approved by the British Electro-technical Approvals Board, and display the BEAB approval mark.

The consumer is legally protected by the Low Voltage Electrical Equipment (Safety) Regulations 1989 which in addition to other safety features require equipment to be designed so that it does not emit a dangerous level of radiation, and it is constructed in accordance with good engineering practice. Microwave ovens are safe providing the manufacturer adheres strictly to the standard and regulations and the consumer uses and maintains the oven in accordance with the manufacturer's instructions. This is of paramount importance since radiation above the level specified can result in damage to health.

Although food gets hot in a microwave oven the container does not. It is better not to use a microwave to warm up a baby's feed since accidents have occurred when infants have been badly scalded internally as a result of this.

45

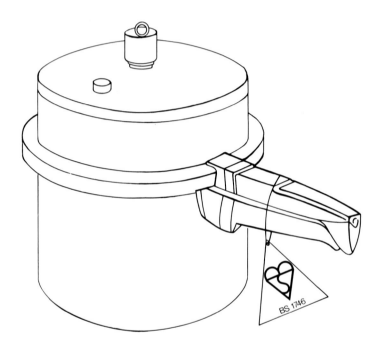

BS 1746

British Standard 1746 is a specification for domestic pressure cookers.

The main requirements of the standard include:

(i) materials

All parts must be made of materials that neither taint food nor make it toxic. Materials must not be affected by contact with foods prepared in the cooker in such a way that the operation or safety of the cooker is impaired. Foods unsuitable for pressure cooking must be identified.

(ii) pressure release devices

A pre-set pressure regulating device maintains the cooker at a selected cooking pressure.

In addition, there must be one or two independent safety pressure relief devices with separate and direct connection from the outside to the interior of the vessel. (If the first safety pressure relief device is not also temperature responsive a second, separate temperature pressure relief device must be fitted). So, there may be three devices fitted: for operating pressure and regulation and for relief of pressure developed if the other device(s) fails.

There are stringent tests to check each of these devices.

(iii) pressure tests

Sample pressure cookers are subject to a proof pressure test. The cooker is connected to a pump and all the remaining openings in the body and lid are sealed. The cooker must then sustain a pressure equal to six times the nominal cooking pressure, without noticeable effect.

In addition the sample is further tested to destruction by subjecting it to a bursting pressure test. Measurement is made of the pressure at which the vessel bursts or is deformed to such an extent that appreciable leakage results.

(iv) information

A
The manufacturer shall plainly and permanently mark the cooker as follows:

(i)   his name or means of identification

(ii)   the number of the British Standard i.e. BS 1746

(iii)   a warning notice in the lid calling attention to the necessity to read the operating instructions before use, e.g. WARNING – READ THE INSTRUCTIONS BEFORE USE

(iv)   the working pressure(s) of the cooker.

B
A comprehensive instruction booklet must be provided.

A manufacturer claiming that his product is made in accordance with the standard may mark it 'MADE TO BS 1746'. But for the right to display the Kitemark the manufacturer must be a licensee and agree to the conditions laid down by BSI.

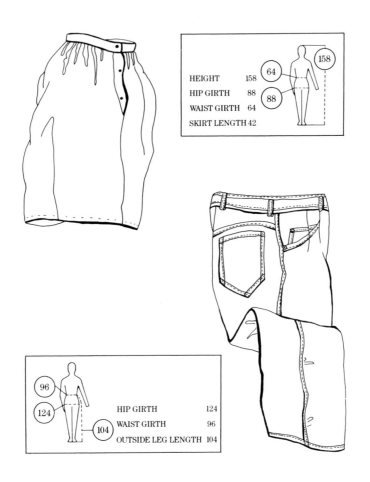

HEIGHT	158
HIP GIRTH	88
WAIST GIRTH	64
SKIRT LENGTH	42

HIP GIRTH	124
WAIST GIRTH	96
OUTSIDE LEG LENGTH	104

SIZE CODING

To help buyers choose the right size, clothing is labelled with body dimensions. There are standards defining the dimensions and others stating which dimensions should be given for a particular garment.

There are separate standards for men's, women's and children's wear. Dimensions for men include chest, waist and neck girth, height and inside leg length. Dimensions for women include bust, underbust, hip and waist girth, height and outside leg length.

The control dimensions for children's and infants' wear are divided into three groups: infants, girls and boys. The basic control dimension is height based on a specified fixed point of 104 cm, with intervals of 6 cm. This is the only control dimension for infants, whereas there are additionally for girls: bust, underbust, hip and waist girth.

Dimensions stated will vary depending on the type of garment. For example, a girl's skirt label should show height, hip and waist girth, whereas a man's jacket will show height, chest and waist girth.

This information can be clearly displayed on a pictogram on the label. Agreement to this standard, ISO 3635, has now been reached by 27 countries, although the pictogram is not in common use in the UK.

PP 787 *Standards and textiles* gives further information on sizing and is available from BSI Sales Department, Linford Wood, Milton Keynes MK14 6LE, price £6.00.

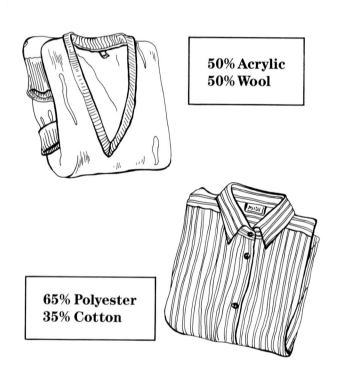

50% Acrylic
50% Wool

65% Polyester
35% Cotton

FIBRE CONTENT

Regulations require that most textile products be labelled with the type and quantity by percentage of different fibres used.

Accordingly, a label should be found stating the various fibres used in the fabric and their content as a percentage of the whole. Fabrics bought by the metre or yard must also have a clear indication of their fibre content at the point-of-sale.

The consumer is protected in this instance by the Textile Products (Indication of Fibre Content) Regulations 1986 and only small items such as watch straps, tobacco pouches and artificial flowers are excluded from the obligation to state fibre content.

Because children's nightdresses and dressing gowns must by law be made from fabrics complying with BS 5722 *Specification for flammability performance of fabrics and fabric assemblies used in sleepwear and dressing gowns* no label referring to flammability is required. However, children's pyjamas or adult nightwear made from fabric which may not necessarily comply must be labelled, to show whether or not it meets the requirements of BS 5722.

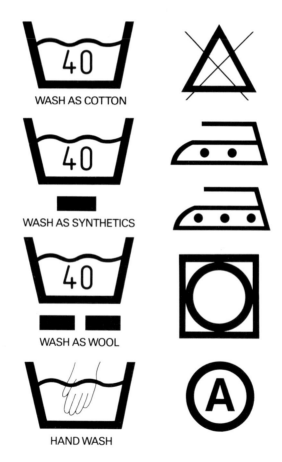

WASH AS COTTON

WASH AS SYNTHETICS

WASH AS WOOL

HAND WASH

CARE LABELLING

CARE LABELLING

BS 2747 *Code of practice for textile care labelling* recommends how information can be passed to the consumer on the washing, bleaching, ironing, dry cleaning and drying of textile articles. The symbols used on the labels are consistent with those used, for example, on detergent packs, washing machines and irons, so that they may be easily understood by the consumer. This is of obvious benefit to both manufacturer and consumer since it should help to reduce misunderstanding between the two parties and prevent inadvertent mis-laundering. It is recommended that only relevant symbols should be shown with a cross through them.

A new addition to the standard is a solid or broken bar which may appear beneath the washtub symbol. The solid bar indicates that a process with reduced mechanical action is recommended and the broken bar, a much reduced mechanical action. Where no bar appears, this means normal mechanical action. To help consumers understand this new symbol explanatory words will be added to the labels for an introductory period.

The symbols shown are just some of the ones found in the standard and have the following meanings:

 machine wash at 40°C, normal mechanical action

 machine wash at 40°C, reduced mechanical action

 machine wash at 40°C, much reduced mechanical action

 hand wash only

 do not bleach

 may be ironed with a warm iron

 may be ironed with a hot iron

 may be tumbled dried

 May be dry cleaned. Other letters and/or a bar beneath the circle indicates the required process to the dry cleaner.

The label itself should be made of a durable material and should be firmly fixed to the garment so that it lasts the lifetime of the particular piece of clothing.

A leaflet on the International Care Labelling Symbols is available free from the Home Laundering Consultative Council, British Apparel Centre, 7 Swallow Place, London W1R 7AA. Tel: 071–408 0020.

53

The International Leather Mark is the sign of real leather as defined in BS 2780:1983 *Glossary of leather terms:* 'Hide or skin with its original fibrous structure more or less intact, tanned to be imputrescible. The hair or wool may or may not have been removed. It is also made from a hide or skin that has been split into layers or segmented either before or after tanning.
Note 1. If the leather has a surface coating, the mean thickness of this surface layer, however applied, must not be more than 0.15 mm.
Note 2. If the tanned hide or skin is disintegrated mechanically and/or chemically into fibrous particles, small pieces or powders and then, with or without the combination of a building agent, is made into sheets or forms, such sheets or forms are not leather.'

The mark was designed by the International Council of Tanners to replace the various national symbols in previous use.

The scheme for the use of leathermarks is run in the UK by the British Leather Confederation.

Manufacturers using the marks, either on products or associated literature are asked to ensure that the labels are only used on products made from leather, as defined above, and not on coated or laminated leather.

The Woolmark is the International Wool Secretariat's (IWS) certification mark for products made from pure new wool. Manufacturers may be licensed by the IWS to use the mark on products, providing they meet an IWS quality specification covering fibre content, change of appearance in wear, durability and dimensional stability.

The IWS acts as a consumer watchdog by monitoring production and factory records and taking random samples for testing. Additionally the IWS buys Woolmarked goods from the shops and performs spot checks.

Various test methods developed by the IWS have been incorporated into national standards and some have been adopted by the International Organization for Standardization.

One of the most recent test methods developed by the IWS is the WRONZ carpet simulator. This machine allows for objective testing of carpets and the simulation of actual wear.

The Woolmark is used world-wide on the majority of a range of consumer products made from wool.

Products	Percentage of goods bearing Woolmark if made wholly or partly of wool
carpets	65%
handknitting yarns	80%
blankets	82%
men's outerwear	65%
women's outerwear	48%
adults knitwear	71%

More than 400 000 000 labels are applied to goods each year. There are over 15 000 licensees in more than 50 countries.

CUSTOMER INFORMATION

Design No.	
Design Name/Colour	
Pile Fibre Content ($\pm 3\%$)	
Widths	
Construction	
Pattern Repeat	
Flammability	
Cleaning Instructions	

THE BRITISH CARPET MANUFACTURERS ASSOCIATION GRADING SCHEME

● INDEPENDENTLY CHECKED FOR PERFORMANCE
● SUBJECT TO PERIODIC TESTING

For additional information please refer to retailer or phone BCMA on 071-734 9853

Also Suitable for Stairs

Kitchen

Bathroom

Use Intensity	Bedroom	Dining Room	Lounge	Hall
Extra Heavy				
Heavy				
Medium				
Light				

Suitable for:

BRITISH STANDARD
7131 : 1989
Classification

© BCMA 1989

CARPET LABELLING

CARPET LABELLING

Carpet labelling is covered by BS 3655 *Recommendations for informative labelling of textile floor coverings.* Carpets should be labelled with the size, construction (e.g. Axminster, Wilton, tufted, fibre-bonded etc), fibre content, cleaning and laying instructions.

Carpets should also describe their performance when subjected to a small ignition source e.g. lighted match, burning cigarette or glowing coal.

BS 7131 *Performance rating of textile floor coverings* specifies and classifies their suitability for use in different locations.

British Carpet Manufacturers' Association Grading Schemes

The British Carpet Manufacturers Association (BCMA) Carpet Grading Scheme is based very closely on BS 7131 which, in turn, was based on the principles established by the BCMA for grading pile carpets.

The BCMA grading scheme is promoted to consumers by a distinctive label. It pictorially shows the areas in a home for which the graded carpet would be suitable. Carpets within the scheme undergo random testing to ensure that quality standards are maintained.

SEAT BELTS

SEAT BELTS

Since January 1983 drivers and front seat passengers have been required to wear seat belts.

The law for rear seats was introduced in September 1989. Children under the age of 14 must wear seat belts in the rear of a car where they are fitted. All cars registered from 1 April 1987 must be fitted with rear seat belts. Wearing properly tested seat belts and restraints saves lives and cuts down the risk of serious injury.

All new seat belts are tested and approved in accordance with the European Commission Directive 77/541 EEC or the equivalent Regulation of the ECE (the Economic Commission for Europe). For this purpose BSI acts as the accredited agent of the Department of Transport. Manufacturers are bound by law to submit their belts for testing.

Among the tests carried out are the following:

(i)   Dynamic tests using a dummy belted to a trolley which is propelled forward so that impact occurs at 50 km/h. The dummy should remain stable within specified limits. Following impact, all parts of the belt are examined for signs of wear or breakage and the buckle is tested to see whether it can be opened with a maximum force of 60 N.

(ii)   Tests for resistance to corrosion.

(iii)   Tests for resistance to chafing of webbing from rigid parts.

(iv)   Correct functioning of the retractor is required even after 40 000 applications. The retractor, a device which is attached to one of the safety belt anchorage points holding a part or the whole of the belt, allows the belt to be pulled out freely except in the event of an accident when it locks automatically.

(v)   Strength tests on straps under various conditions.

What to look for :

- BSI's Kitemark shows that the product meets the British Standard.

- 'e' shows that the product meets the standards set down in the European Commission Directive.

- An 'E' mark shows that the product complies with the Economic Commission for Europe's regulations drawn up through the United Nations.

Both marks are followed by a distinguishing letter or number of the Member state of the EEC. In the case of the United Kingdom this number is 11.

Other markings indicate the type of belt and the component type approval number.

Until February 1979 every UK tested and installed seat belt carried the BS Kitemark as manufacturers were bound by law to comply with BS 3254 *Seat belt assemblies for motor vehicles*. This is now only used for replacement or repair of previously Kitemarked belts.

A further free leaflet giving information and advice on children's safety in cars is available from the Education Section, BSI, Linford Wood, Milton Keynes. MK14 6LE. Tel (0908) 220022

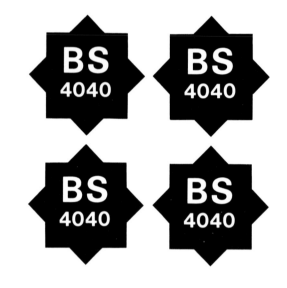

STAR MARKING OF PETROL PUMPS

STAR MARKING OF PETROL PUMPS

To ensure that motorists buy the right sort of petrol for their car, petrol pumps in the UK are 'star'-marked. This system is derived from BS 4040 *Leaded petrol (gasoline) for motor vehicles* which gives the requirements for three grades of leaded petrol. The vehicle manufacturer will recommend the minimum 'star' grading for petrol for the car concerned. Unlike other EEC countries, there are regulations in the UK making it compulsory to follow the standard, and retailers must display the 'star' grading of petrol clearly on pumps and selector buttons.

UNLEADED PETROL

UNLEADED PETROL

However, leaded petrol is on the way out. A newcomer to the garage forecourt is the pump for unleaded petrol, which is gradually being introduced throughout the UK as more vehicles are designed or adapted to run on unleaded fuel. Because most conventional engines need leaded fuel to run properly and can be damaged by unleaded petrol, it is especially important that these new pumps should be clearly distinguishable from 'star' marked pumps. The standard requires that the word 'unleaded' should be shown, preferably on a green background, together with the number BS 7070 and grade designation: 'Premium' or 'Regular'. In 1989 new legislation came into force requiring all new cars to be designed to run on unleaded petrol.

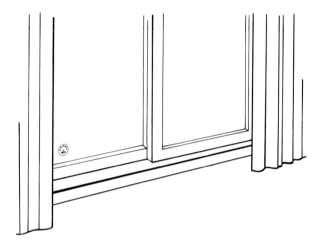

KEY

E. Clarke Plc – Manufacturer

L – Type of glazing
   (L – laminated)
   (T – toughened)

BS 6206 – British Standard Number

B – Class of glazing

SAFETY GLAZING

SAFETY GLAZING

Modern buildings now use far more glass in far larger panels than in the past. Large glazed areas may be found in internal doors, picture windows, shower areas, sports halls and schools.

When safety glazing, manufactured to BS 6206 *Impact performance requirements for flat safety glass and safety plastics for use in buildings*, is used for windows or doors it is marked in the corner in a similar manner to the markings usually found on car windows showing :

(i)   the name or trade mark of the manufacturer
(ii) the type of glass e.g. toughened or laminated
(iii) the number of the British Standard − BS 6206
(iv) the classification of glazing used.

In order to test safety glazing, a 45 kg weight, evolved from the weight of a running child, is swung against the glass from increasing heights. The material is then classified according to its success rate in the following way :

Class	Behaviour on impact		
	Drop height 305 mm	Drop height 457 mm	Drop height 1219 mm
A	No breakage, or breaks safely	No breakage, or breaks safely	No breakage, breaks safely
B	No breakage, or breaks safely	No breakage, or breaks safely	No requirement
C	No breakage, or breaks safely	No requirement	No requirement

Recommendations in BS 6262 *Code of practice for glazing for buildings* include, amongst others, all fully glazed doors and door sidepanels (which includes most patio doors, and low-level glazing in high pedestrian traffic locations) to be fitted with safety glazing in order to reduce the risk of injury from 'impact accidents' to a minimum.

Depending on the size of the panel a particular class of glazing is recommended. For example, for doors wider than 900 mm class B glazing is recommended; for doors less than 900 mm wide, but with a glazed area wider than 300 mm, class C glazing is recommended.

Annealed glass, often known as sheet, float or plate glass is adequate in many situations providing the correct thickness is used for the location and pane size. The big drawback is that it is brittle. When it breaks it produces sharp jagged pieces often causing deep lacerations in the hands, arms or other parts of the body.

Although the number of accidents associated with glass in the home is comparatively small the results are often tragic and permanent scarring is frequent. By choosing the correct type of safety glazing for high-risk areas many of these accidents could be avoided.

Manufacturers' tradenames and marks can be identified from the Register of Safety Glazing marks which is available for inspection from the Glass and Glazing Federation, 44-48 Borough High Street, London. SE11 1XB Tel: 071 − 403 7177.